ERA
FOR BEGINNERS

Writers and Readers

WRITERS AND READERS PUBLISHING, INC.
P.O. BOX 461, VILLAGE STATION
NEW YORK, NEW YORK 10014

TEXT AND DESIGN COPYRIGHT © 1991 ERROL SELKIRK
COVER DESIGN © SUSAN WILLMARTH
LETTERING AND DESIGN CONSULTATION: DARYL LONG

A WRITERS AND READERS DOCUMENTARY COMIC BOOK
COPYRIGHT © 1991

ISBN
0-86316-141-3

1 2 3 4 5 6 7 8 9 10 0

MANUFACTURED IN THE UNITED STATES OF AMERICA

BEGINNER'S DOCUMENTARY COMIC BOOKS ARE
PUBLISHED BY WRITERS AND READERS PUBLISHING, INC.
ITS TRADEMARK, CONSISTING OF THE WORDS
"FOR BEGINNERS, WRITERS AND READERS DOCUMENTARY
COMIC BOOKS," AND THE WRITERS AND READERS
LOGO, IS REGISTERED IN THE U.S. PATENT AND
TRADEMARK OFFICE AND IN OTHER COUNTRIES.

EROTICA FOR BEGINNERS

WRITTEN AND DESIGNED BY ERROL SELKIRK

LETTERING BY Daryl Long

THIS BOOK IS DEDICATED TO

DEBRA JOY

"I SING THE BODY ELECTRIC..."

WHERE THE BOUNDARIES END, THE EROTIC BEGINS. EROTICISM PENETRATES THE BARRIER BETWEEN REASON AND FEELING, BETWEEN THE INDIVIDUAL AND THE WORLD. LIKE A DEEP RELIGIOUS EXPERIENCE, PASSION HAS THE POWER TO TRANSPORT US OUTSIDE OUR EVERYDAY SELVES.

THE PASSION OF LOVE AND LOVE MAKING IS THE THEME OF *EROTICA*. THROUGHOUT HISTORY, ARTISTS HAVE EXPLORED THE EROTIC IMAGINATION AS A WAY OF UNDERSTANDING THE UNION OF OPPOSITES WHICH IS THE BASIS OF EXISTENCE-- THE SELF AND THE WORLD, MALE AND FEMALE, SPIRIT AND MATTER, LIGHT AND DARK, LIFE AND DEATH.

SOME
CULTURES
CELEBRATE
PASSION AS
A NATURAL
PHENOMENON,
SOMETHING
AS BASIC AS
BIRTH, GROWTH,
AND AGING.
OTHERS
EMPLOY EROTIC
SYMBOLS TO
PLUNGE INTO
THE HIDDEN
MYSTERIES OF
THE
SUBCONSCIOUS,
OF DREAMS AND
FANTASIES.

EROTICA HAS ALSO BEEN USED TO POKE FUN AT FALSE MODESTY, AND TO UNDERSCORE THE AWKWARD SEXUAL DEPENDENCY THAT LINKS MEN AND WOMEN.

IN THE HANDS OF SOCIAL
CRITICS, EROTICA HAS
REVEALED THE WAY THAT
PEOPLE TREAT --
OR MISTREAT --
EACH OTHER IN OTHER
AREAS OF LIFE.
CLEARLY,
SEXUAL RELATIONS
OFTEN MIRROR SOCIAL
RELATIONS.

EROTICA HAS SOMETIMES SERVED TO
RE-CREATE THE LOST INNOCENCE
OF CHILDHOOD. AND FOR THOSE WHOSE
PASSIONS FALL OUTSIDE THE
MAINSTREAM OF SOCIETY,
THE EROTIC HAS BEEN
A WAY TO EXPLORE
THE LIMITS OF
OBSESSION AND
TRANSGRESSION.

Passion

SHATTERS THE SMUG, SELF-CONTAINED PERSON-
ALITY WE LIKE TO SHOW THE WORLD. SEXUAL
ECSTACY FORCES US TO COME FACE TO FACE
WITH THE IRRATIONAL.

FEW ARTISTS HAVE MADE EROTICA THEIR WHOLE
REASON FOR BEING. MOST HAVE CREATED SEXU-
ALLY-ORIENTED WORKS OUT OF A NEED TO SHOW
THE TOTALITY OF HUMAN EXPERIENCE.

REGARDLESS OF CULTURE, GENUINE EROTICA REVEALS

THREE IMPORTANT CHARACTERISTICS:

- IT IS ART ON A SEXUAL THEME, NOT SIMPLY A
  REPRESENTATION OF SEX. EROTICA REFLECTS
  PASSIONS AS WELL AS ACTS.

- IT CAN BE JUSTIFIED ON ARTISTIC GROUNDS. EROTICA IS
  GOOD ART WHICH DEMONSTRATES SKILL AND IMAGI-
  NATION. IT HAS AN EMOTIONAL RICHNESS WHICH
  CONTINUES TO IMPRESS AND EXCITE LONG AFTER
  VIEWING.

- AND FINALLY, EROTICA CONTAINS IDEAS.

EROTIC ART TELLS US MUCH ABOUT HUMAN
REACTIONS TO HUMAN ACTS, ABOUT HOW THE ARTIST
VIEWS PASSION, LOVE,
AND THE
WORLD.

FOR TOO LONG, EROTICA HAS BEEN A LOST CHAPTER IN OUR HISTORY, A SUBJECT FOR JOKES AND KNOWING WINKS. MANY PEOPLE TODAY STILL BELIEVE THAT LOVE-MAKING IS FAR TOO PERSONAL A SUBJECT TO BE EXPOSED PUBLICLY IN A PAINTING OR BOOK.

YET IN OTHER PLACES AND TIMES, THE EROTIC WAS VALUED AS A LINK BETWEEN THE HUMAN AND THE DIVINE.

EVERY PIECE OF EROTICA OFFERS A CHALLENGE. IT IS NOT ENOUGH TO PEEK THROUGH THE KEYHOLE. OPEN THE DOOR AND EXPERIENCE.

UMANS HAVE ALWAYS CREATED IMAGES. AS A SPECIES, WE SEEM TO HAVE A NEED TO USE ART TO DEPICT THE WORLD AROUND US, AS WELL AS THE WAY WE FEEL ABOUT THAT WORLD IN RELATION TO OURSELVES.

TWENTY-FIVE THOUSAND YEARS BEFORE THE FIRST WRITTEN WORD, A STONE AGE ARTIST CARVED THIS STATUE OF A FEMALE WITH SWELLING BREASTS AND BUTTOCKS. LIKE HUNDREDS OF OTHER SIMILAR FIGURINES FOUND THROUGHOUT THE WORLD, IT WAS FACELESS.

NOTHING COULD HAVE BEEN MORE IMPORTANT AT A TIME WHEN PEOPLE DIDN'T YET UNDERSTAND THE CONNECTION BETWEEN SEX AND PREGNANCY, WHEN CHILDBIRTH WAS A MYSTERY AND WHEN SURVIVAL WAS DEPENDENT UPON THE LUCK OF THE HUNT.

WERE THESE VENUSES A KIND OF FERTILITY MAGIC?
WAS VIEWING AND HANDLING THEM A WAY TO
STIMULATE SEXUAL DESIRE? PERHAPS, BUT
WHAT IS CLEAR IS THAT PASSION IS ONE
OF THE BIOLOGICAL STRATEGIES
FOR HUMAN SURIVIVAL:
MAKING PLEASURABLE
WHAT IS
NECESSARY.

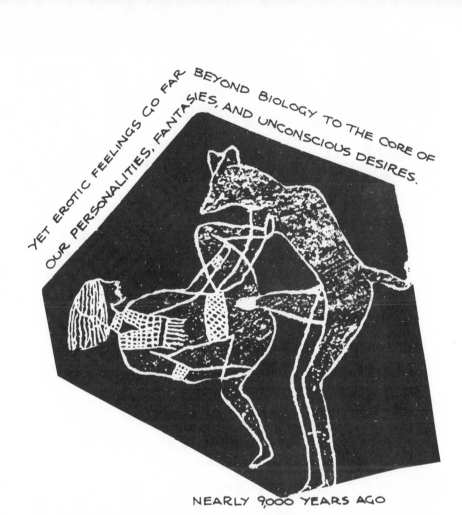

YET EROTIC FEELINGS GO FAR BEYOND BIOLOGY TO THE CORE OF OUR PERSONALITIES, FANTASIES, AND UNCONSCIOUS DESIRES.

NEARLY 9,000 YEARS AGO
SOMEONE SCRATCHED THIS PICTURE ON A ROCK WALL IN FEZZAN, NORTH AFRICA. IT SHOWS INTERCOURSE BETWEEN A WOMAN AND A SEMI-HUMAN CREATURE WITH A DOG'S HEAD AND AN ENORMOUS PENIS.

DID THIS REPRESENT A NIGHT-MARE, SOME KIND OF MAGIC, OR A SEXUAL RITUAL PER-FORMED BY A MASKED PRIEST? THE ANSWER IS LOST IN TIME. YET IT POINTS TO A DARKER SIDE OF THE EROTIC IMAGINATION THAT DATES BACK TO THE DAWN OF CONSCIOUSNESS.

15

NOT FAR AWAY IN
EGYPT A GREAT
CIVILIZATION WAS
BEGINNING TO DEVELOP
ALONG THE FERTILE
BANKS OF THE RIVER
NILE. IT WAS ONE OF
THE FIRST SOCIETIES TOTALLY BASED ON
AGRICULTURE, NOT HUNTING AND GATHERING.

THE

EGYPTIANS

VIEWED SEX AS A

MODEL FOR THE CREATION

OF THE WORLD. MYTHS TOLD OF HOW

THE SKY AND EARTH WERE DRAWN TOGETHER

═══════ BY THE EROTIC FORCE, DESIRE═══════

THE EGYPTIAN
LIFE SYMBOL--
THE ANKH--
MAY VERY WELL
HAVE SYMBOLIZED
THE UNION OF
MALE AND
FEMALE
ORGANS.

EGYPTIAN ART ABOUNDS WITH EROTIC IMAGES. WILD FERTILITY CELEBRATIONS WERE HELD TO MARK THE PLANTING OF THE SEED AND THE HARVEST. FOREMOST AMONG THE GODS AND GODDESSES WAS ISIS, PASSIONATE EARTH MOTHER AND

PROTECTOR. IT WAS UNDER HER INFLUENCE, PERHAPS, THAT THE FIRST LOVE POEM IN EXISTENCE WAS WRITTEN NEARLY 3,500 YEARS AGO:

"CAN ANYTHING BE SWEETER THAN THIS HOUR WHEN I AM WITH YOU AND MY HEART SOARS? FOR WHEN YOU VISIT ME, DO WE NOT EMBRACE AND FONDLE EACH OTHER AND SURRENDER OURSELVES TO DELIGHT? IF YOU DESIRE TO CARESS MY THIGH I WILL OFFER YOU MY BREAST AS WELL, FOR I AM WITH YOU AND YOU LIFT MY HEART."

ANOTHER GREAT CIVILIZATION WAS NOW ALSO
DEVELOPING IN MESOPOTAMIA -- THE LAND
BETWEEN THE RIVERS TIGRIS AND EUPHRATES
IN PRESENT DAY IRAQ. AND ONCE AGAIN, THE
POWER OF SEXUAL PASSION WAS LINKED WITH
FERTILITY.

EARLY MYTHS TOLD HOW THE EARTH
GODDESS WAS JOINED IN "SACRED MARRIAGE" WITH
THE POTENT YOUNG GOD, WHO WAS SYMBOLIZED BY
THE BULL AND THE THUNDER THAT BROUGHT THE
RAIN TO WATER THE CROPS, SEXUAL RITUALS
CELEBRATED THE DIVINE UNION ON WHICH LIFE
DEPENDED:

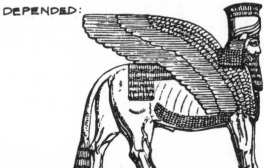

"MY PRECIOUS CARESS
IS MORE DELICIOUS
THAN HONEY... LET
ME CARESS YOU."

THE GODDESS WAS
OFTEN REPRESENTED
BY THE CRESENT MOON,
THE SYMBOL OF FEMALE
PERIODICITY, AS WELL AS
BY THE BRIGHT MORNING
STAR, VENUS. AND
SINCE HER
BEGUILING POWERS
REACHED FROM
HEAVEN DEEP INTO THE
VERY CORE OF THE
EARTH, THE GODDESS
WAS OFTEN SHOWN WITH
A SACRED TREE AND A SERPENT
FOR A COMPANION.

IN THE BUSTLING CITY OF
BABYLON, THE GODDESS
LOST SOME OF HER FERTILE
EARTHINESS AS SHE WAS
TRANSFORMED INTO
THE ALLURING
GODDESS
OF
LOVE:
ISHTAR.

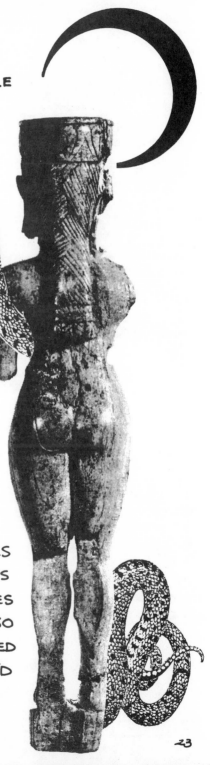

"ISHTAR IS
CLOTHED WITH
PLEASURE AND LOVE,"
SANG THE OLD HYMNS.
"SHE IS LADEN
WITH VITALITY,
CHARM, AND
VOLUPTUOUSNESS...
IN LIPS SHE IS
SWEET, LIFE IS
HER MOUTH."

ACCORDINGLY, PRIESTESSES
SERVED IN HER TEMPLE AS
RITUAL PROSTITUTES. RITES
IN HER HONOR WERE ALSO
ECSTATICALLY CELEBRATED
ON HILLTOPS AND SACRED
GROVES ACROSS THE
MIDDLE EAST.

"THOU SHALT MAKE THEE NO MOLTEN GODS... LEST THOU MAKE A COVENANT WITH THE INHABITANTS OF THE LAND AND THEY GO A WHORING AFTER THEIR GODS...."

THE ISRAELITES THAT MOSES LED INTO THE LAND OF CANAAN WERE THE DESCENDANTS OF NOMADIC HERDERS, NOT FARMERS. FOR THEM SACRED SEX COULD NEVER BE THE MODEL OF HOW THEIR UNIVERSE WORKED. THE EARTH WAS NO BEAUTIFUL GODDESS. IT WAS A GRASSY SURFACE THAT FED THEIR FLOCKS. AND GOD WAS A JEALOUS MALE DIETY WHO LIVED ALONE HIGH ON A VOLCANIC MOUNTAIN, AND WHO CREATED PEOPLE, LIKE POTTERY, OUT OF LIFELESS CLAY.

"HIS LEFT HAND IS UNDER MY HEAD,
AND HIS RIGHT HAND DOTH EMBRACE ME...

LET HIM KISS ME WITH KISSES OF
HIS MOUTH: FOR LOVE IS
BETTER
THAN
WINE...."

ONCE IN THE

PROMISED LAND, THE ISRAELITES BECAME

FARMERS. THE SEDUCTIVE WORSHIP OF THE FERTILITY

GODDESS NOW MADE MORE SENSE TO THE PEOPLE THAN

THE RELIGION OF THE OLD SKY GOD. PROPHETS AROSE

OVER THE CENTURIES TO COMBAT THE SEXUAL RITES

OF ASTARTE, THE LOCAL VERSION OF ISHTAR.

EVENTUALLY, THE SYMBOLS OF THE GODDESS WERE

INCORPORATED INTO JEWISH SCRIPTURE -- WITH A

DIFFERENCE. THE SERPENT BECAME THE

DEVIL, SACRED SEX BECAME SIN, AND

THE TREE OF LIFE BECAME

TEMPTATION AND

THE CAUSE OF MAN'S FALL FROM GRACE.

ACROSS THE MEDITERRANEAN SEA, ANOTHER INVASION OF NOMADS DESTROYED THE HIGHLY REFINED CULTURE THAT HAD DEVELOPED ON THE ISLAND OF CRETE.

HERE IN KNOSOS, YOUNG MEN WOULD LEAP OVER SACRED BULLS IN RITUAL SPORT, WHILE BARECHESTED PRIESTESSES WORSHIPPED THE GREAT MOTHER WITH SONG AND SACRIFICE. TRACES OF THE ANCIENT BULL CULT ENDURE IN THE MYTH OF THE **MINOTAUR** -- BORN OF A QUEEN WHO MATED WITH A BULL. THIS STRANGE CREATURE DWELLED IN THE LABYRINTH BENEATH THE ROYAL PALACE AND REQUIRED HUMAN SACRIFICE.

THEN AROUND 1500 B.C., NOMAD HERDERS KNOWN AS **GREEKS**, CONQUERED CRETE. LIKE THE ISRAELITES, THEY WORSHIPPED A POWERFUL SKY GOD. HIS NAME WAS ZEUS, AND HE RULED BY THE FORCE OF LIGHTNING BOLTS HURLED FROM HIS HOME ON MOUNT OLYMPUS.

ZEUS WAS SURROUNDED BY A HOST OF IMMORTALS WHO REFLECTED THE LIFE AND VALUES OF THIS RUDE WARRIOR SOCIETY. WHILE THE ROLE OF WOMEN WAS REDUCED, MALE SEXUALITY WAS CELEBRATED BY THE ERECTION OF PHALLIC TOTEMS CALLED **HERMES**. THESE WERE PLACED IN FRONT OF HOMES AND ALONG THE ROAD.

APHRODITE WAS THE GREEK GODDESS OF LOVE. BORN OF SEAFOAM FORMED FROM THE SEVERED GENITALS OF THE GOD OF TIME, SHE WAS PURE DESIRE. EMERGING FROM THE WAVES, "... *HER DELICATE BOSOM SHOWN LIKE THE MOON.*"

HER COMPANION WAS A MISCHIEVOUS
CHILD NAMED EROS, WHOSE ARROWS
STIRRED THE PASSION OF ALL.

APHRODITE WAS DESIRED BY THE GODS, PRAYED TO BY NEWLYWED WOMEN, AND HAILED AS THE PROTECTORESS OF PROSTITUTES. HUNDREDS OF PRIESTESSES SERVED IN HER TEMPLE AT CORINTH, WHERE SEXUAL GRATIFICATION AND RITUAL DEVOTION WENT HAND IN HAND.

PROSTITUTES, IN FACT, WERE THE ONLY RELATIVELY FREE WOMEN IN GREECE. MOST WOMEN WERE RAISED TO BE GOOD MOTHERS AND OBEDIENT WIVES.

THEY WERE KEPT INDOORS AND ONLY WENT ABOUT WHEN PROPERLY VEILED AND CHAPERONED.

YET, PROSTITUTES WERE ALLOWED TO MANAGE
THEIR OWN AFFAIRS AND FINANCES. LIKE
JAPANESE GEISHAS, THE HIGHEST CLASS OF
COURTESANS WERE WEALTHY, WELL-EDUCATED,
AND SKILLED IN MUSIC, CONVERSATION, AND
LOVE-MAKING. THEY SERVED AS THE MODEL
FOR MANY OF THE EROTIC SCENES FOUND ON
GREEK POTTERY AND PLATES.

BY 500 B.C., THE GREEKS
WERE PRODUCING VAST AMOUNTS OF EROTIC
ART. SOCIETY HAD OUTGROWN ITS RURAL
ROOTS. IN THE CITIES, PHILOSOPHY AND SCIENCE
NOW MADE MORE SENSE THAN THE OLD
NATURE MYTHS. SEXUAL PLEASURE TOO LOST
ITS CONNECTION TO FERTILITY; PLEASURE
BECAME AN END IN ITSELF. AND
ALL THE ARTS SOON
REFLECTED THIS FACT.

" LET US WAIT AT HOME
WITH OUR FACES MADE
UP AND THEN ADVANCE
TO GREET OUR HUSBANDS
WITH NOTHING ON BUT
OUR LITTLE TUNICS...
THEN WHEN THEY ARE
PANTING WITH DESIRE,
IF WE SLIP AWAY INSTEAD
OF YIELDING, THEY'LL
SOON CONCLUDE AN
ARMISTICE.... "

IN THE THEATRE, DRAMATIST
ARISTOPHENES
BLENDED SEX AND POLITICS IN
HIS BRILLIANT COMEDIES. IN
LYSISTRATA, THE BEAUTIFUL
HEROINE PERSUADES THE WOMEN OF
ATHENS TO ABSTAIN FROM
SEX
UNTIL THEIR HUSBANDS AGREE
TO END A DISASTROUS
WAR.

THE PENT-UP DESIRES OF GREEK WOMEN FOUND RELEASE IN AN ECSTATIC NEW RELIGION. DIONYSUS, THE HANDSOME YOUNG GOD OF WINE, HAD DIED AND WAS REBORN LIKE THE GRAPE VINE AT THE COMING OF SPRING.

TO CELEBRATE THIS MIRACLE, NOISY PROCESSIONS SUMMONED FEMALE WORSHIPPERS FROM THEIR HOMES TO THE HILLTOPS, WHERE

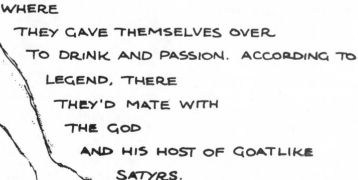

THEY GAVE THEMSELVES OVER TO DRINK AND PASSION. ACCORDING TO LEGEND, THERE THEY'D MATE WITH THE GOD AND HIS HOST OF GOATLIKE SATYRS.

"MY SOUL WHEN I KISSED AGATHON CREPT UP TO MY LIPS AS THOUGH IT WISHED--POOR THING--TO CROSS OVER TO HIM."

THE TRUTH WAS THAT GREEK MEN AND WOMEN WERE TWO SEPARATE SOCIETIES WITH LITTLE IN COMMON. FOR LOVE, SOME MEN TURNED TO THEIR OWN SEX. THEIR MODEL MAY HAVE BEEN ZEUS HIMSELF, WHO WAS SO STRUCK BY THE BEAUTY OF THE BOY GANYMEDE, THAT HE ASSUMED THE FORM OF AN EAGLE AND CARRIED HIM TO HEAVEN. MUCH OF GREEK EROTIC ART WAS DEDICATED TO SCENES OF HOMOSEXUAL DESIRE.

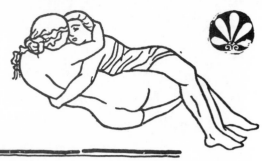

WOMEN, TOO, FELT THE ATTRACTION OF
THEIR OWN SEX. IT IS SAID THAT ON
THE GREEK ISLAND OF LESBOS, THE
POETESS SAPPHO WROTE HER MOST
BEAUTIFUL AND POIGNANT LINES:

"... HEARING YOU SWEETLY
TALKING
AND YOUR SEXY LAUGH
MAKES MY HEART FLY UP
IN MY BREAST.
LOOKING AT YOU EVEN A
SECOND,
MY VOICE WON'T COME
ANY MORE...
A LITTLE FIRE RUNS UP
AND OVER MY SKIN:
MY EYES CAN'T SEE, MY
EARS THEY ROAR...
AND I SEEM
LIKE I
COULD
DIE."

"IF THERE IS ANYONE WHO THINKS THAT YOUNG MEN SHOULD BE FORBIDDEN TO MAKE LOVE, EVEN TO PROSTITUTES, HE IS... OUT OF TOUCH NOT ONLY WITH WHAT IS HAPPENING TODAY, BUT EVEN WITH THE WAYS OF OUR FATHERS. FOR WHEN WAS IT NOT CUSTOMARY?"

IN ROME, AS THE QUOTE BY THE NOBLE **CICERO** SHOWS, THE APPROACH TO PASSION WAS STRICTLY DOWN TO EARTH. HERE GREEK IDEAS BLENDED WITH RURAL CHARACTER OF THE PEOPLE. ROMANS, LIKE GOOD, PRACTICAL COUNTRY FOLK, HAD THEIR OWN GOD--PRIAPUS--WITH HIS SWOLLEN MEMBER ADORNING STATUES AND GOOD LUCK AMULETS.

WITH ROMAN MEN CONSTANTLY AWAY AT WAR,
ROMAN WOMEN WERE ABLE TO SEIZE A
GREAT DEAL OF FREEDOM, SOCIAL AND
SEXUAL. FOR YOUNG LOVERS, THE POET
OVID WROTE A SEX MANUAL CALLED THE
ART OF LOVE. IT TOOK A TYPICALLY
PRAGMATIC APPROACH TO THE WHOLE
TOPIC:

"BELIEVE ME, LOVE'S BLISS MUST NOT BE EXHAUSTED. BUT GRADUALLY LURED ON BY SLOW DELAY. WHEN YOU HAVE FOUND THE PLACE WHERE A WOMAN LIKES TO BE TOUCHED, LET NOT SHAME PREVENT YOU FROM TOUCHING...

"BUT NEITHER DO YOU, SPREADING TOO FULL SAIL, LEAVE YOUR MISTRESS BEHIND, NOR LET HER OUTSTRIP YOUR SPEED. HASTE SIDE BY SIDE TO THE GOAL; THEN IS PLEASURE COMPLETE, WHEN MAN AND WOMAN LIE VANQUISHED TOGETHER.

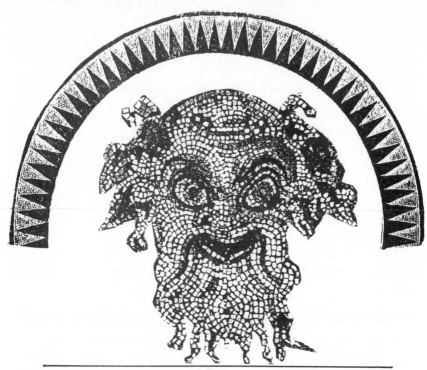

THE SHIFT FROM A REPUBLIC TO AN EMPIRE BROUGHT MANY CHANGES TO ROME. WITH SLAVES TO DO THE WORK AND GREAT WEALTH POURING IN FROM THE PROVINCES, MANY ROMANS HAD NOTHING TO DO BUT AMUSE THEMSELVES. THOSE AT THE TOP WERE GUILTY OF THE GREATEST EXCESSES: EMPEROR TIBERIUS DEBAUCHED CHILDREN, MAD CALIGULA IMPREGNATED HIS SISTER AND MURDERED HER, AND EMPRESS MESSALINA DISGUISED HERSELF AS A COMMON PROSTITUTE TO SATISFY HER DESIRES.

SEX WAS PURSUED RELENTLESSLY TO COMBAT BOREDOM. THE WRITER **PETRONIUS** BRILLIANTLY DESCRIBED HIS SOCIETY'S SLIDE INTO DECADENCE.

IN HIS NOVEL, *THE SATYRICON*, A DISSOLUTE YOUTH STUMBLES INTO A SECRET FERTILITY RITE AND IS PUNISHED BY LOSING HIS POTENCY.

HIS LOVER, A BEAUTIFUL YOUTH, IS STOLEN BY A RIVAL. TO RECOVER HIS POWERS, THE HERO TRAVELS THE LENGTHS OF THE EMPIRE -- A SURREALISTIC REALM PEOPLED BY HERMAPHRODITES, FLAGELLATING EUNUCHS AND EROTOMANIACS OF ALL PERSUASIONS.

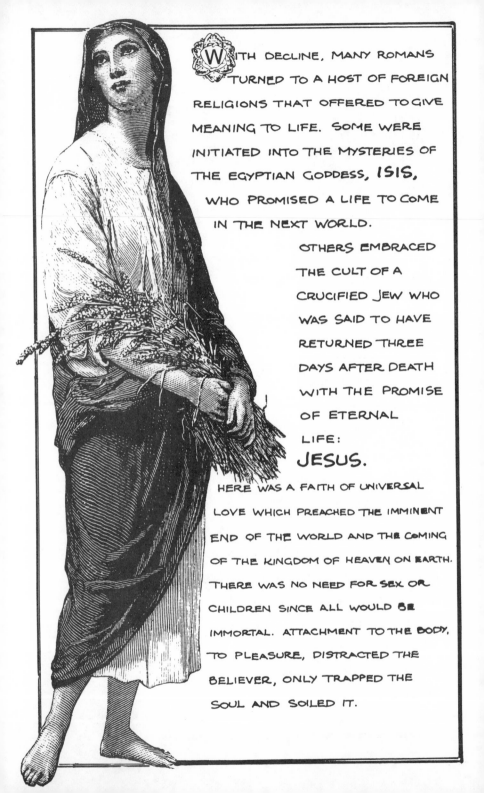

WITH DECLINE, MANY ROMANS TURNED TO A HOST OF FOREIGN RELIGIONS THAT OFFERED TO GIVE MEANING TO LIFE. SOME WERE INITIATED INTO THE MYSTERIES OF THE EGYPTIAN GODDESS, ISIS, WHO PROMISED A LIFE TO COME IN THE NEXT WORLD.

OTHERS EMBRACED THE CULT OF A CRUCIFIED JEW WHO WAS SAID TO HAVE RETURNED THREE DAYS AFTER DEATH WITH THE PROMISE OF ETERNAL LIFE: JESUS.

HERE WAS A FAITH OF UNIVERSAL LOVE WHICH PREACHED THE IMMINENT END OF THE WORLD AND THE COMING OF THE KINGDOM OF HEAVEN ON EARTH. THERE WAS NO NEED FOR SEX OR CHILDREN SINCE ALL WOULD BE IMMORTAL. ATTACHMENT TO THE BODY, TO PLEASURE, DISTRACTED THE BELIEVER, ONLY TRAPPED THE SOUL AND SOILED IT.

YET, THE WORLD DID NOT END AS PROMISED. STILL, THE CHURCH CONTINUED TO MAINTAIN ITS HOSTILITY TO EROS. CELIBACY WAS PROCLAIMED SUPERIOR TO MARRIAGE AND FAMILY. SAINTS AND THEOLOGIANS LAUNCHED UNCEASING ATTACKS ON WOMEN -- SHAMELESS CREATURES WHOSE VERY EXISTENCE LURED CHRISTIANS INTO CARNAL SIN.

"WOMAN, YOU ARE THE DEVIL'S DOORWAY... IT WAS YOUR FAULT THAT THE SON OF GOD HAD TO DIE; YOU SHOULD ALWAYS GO IN MOURNING AND RAGS."

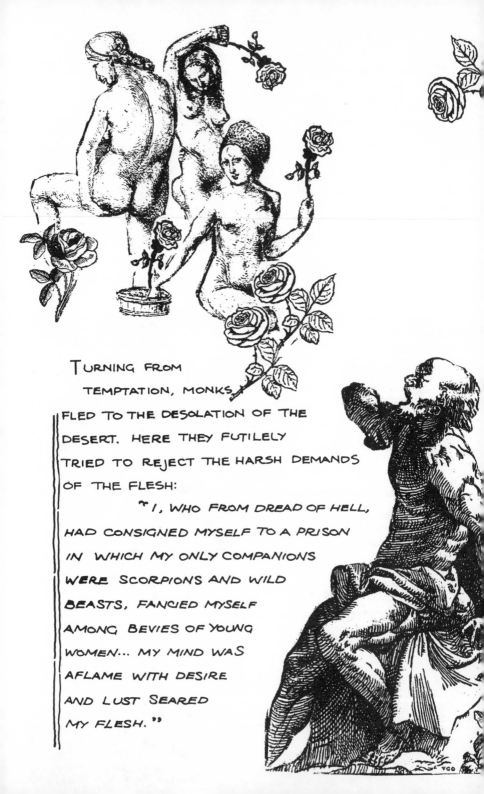

Turning from temptation, monks fled to the desolation of the desert. Here they futilely tried to reject the harsh demands of the flesh:

"I, who from dread of hell, had consigned myself to a prison in which my only companions were scorpions and wild beasts, fancied myself among bevies of young women... my mind was aflame with desire and lust seared my flesh."

"I LOVE CHRIST INTO WHOSE BED I HAVE ENTERED."

IT WAS THIS SAME **SAINT JEROME** WHO ENCOURAGED YOUNG GIRLS TO OFFER THEIR VIRGINITY AS A SACRIFICE TO GOD. AS NUNS THEY WOULD BECOME TRUE BRIDES OF CHRIST.

"JESUS WILL COME BEHIND THE WALL AND HE WILL PUT HIS HAND THROUGH THE OPENING AND WILL TOUCH YOUR BODY. YOU WILL ARISE TREMBLING AND SAY, 'I LANGUISH WITH LOVE.'"

43

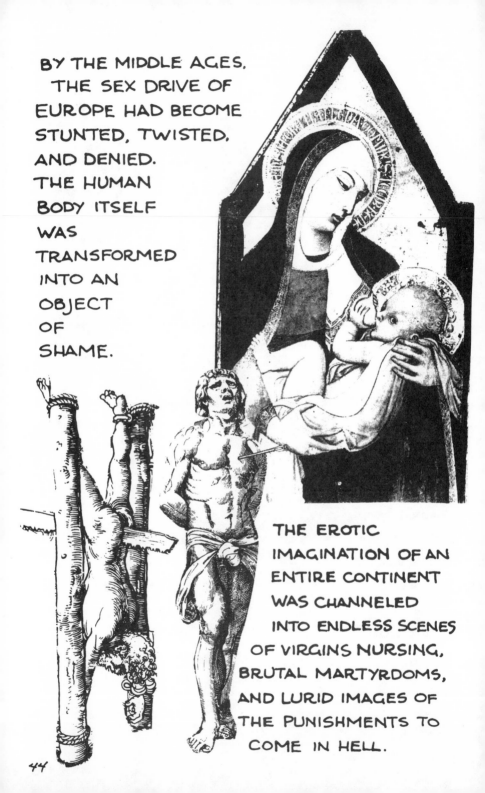

BY THE MIDDLE AGES, THE SEX DRIVE OF EUROPE HAD BECOME STUNTED, TWISTED, AND DENIED. THE HUMAN BODY ITSELF WAS TRANSFORMED INTO AN OBJECT OF SHAME.

THE EROTIC IMAGINATION OF AN ENTIRE CONTINENT WAS CHANNELED INTO ENDLESS SCENES OF VIRGINS NURSING, BRUTAL MARTYRDOMS, AND LURID IMAGES OF THE PUNISHMENTS TO COME IN HELL.

44

DURING THESE DARK AGES,
CIVILIZATION IN EUROPE NEARLY
DISAPPEARED. FEW COULD READ. TRADE
SHRANK, CITIES WERE DESERTED.

IN 1096, RESTLESS CHRISTIAN KNIGHTS LAUNCHED A CRUSADE WHICH CONQUERED JERUSALEM AND THE HOLY LAND FROM THE INFIDEL MUSLIMS. HERE THE BARBAROUS EUROPEANS DISCOVERED A RICH, ANCIENT CULTURE WITH A RADICALLY DIFFERENT VIEW OF THE PLEASURES OF THIS WORLD. FOR THE PROPHET MOHAMMAD WAS NO ASCETIC. AND THE RELIGION HE FOUNDED PRAISED THE LOVE OF WOMEN BY MEN AS A TASTE OF PARADISE TO COME.

IN THE REMARKABLE
COLLECTION OF TALES KNOWN
AS THE *THOUSAND AND
ONE ARABIAN NIGHTS*, WE
READ SENSUAL DESCRIPTIONS
SUCH AS THESE:

"SHE

HATH

BREASTS

LIKE TWO GLOBES OF IVORY, LIKE GOLDEN
POMEGRANATES, BEAUTIFULLY UPRIGHT, ARCHED
AND AND ROUNDED, FIRM AS STONE TO THE
TOUCH, WITH   NIPPLES   ERECT AND
OUTWARD JUTTING.   SHE HATH THIGHS
                    LIKE UNTO PILLARS
                    OF ALABASTER, &
                    BETWEEN THEM
                    THERE VAUNTS A
                    SECRET PLACE, A
                    SACHET OF MUSK, THAT
                    SWELLS, THAT THROBS,
                    THAT IS MOIST AND
                    AVID."

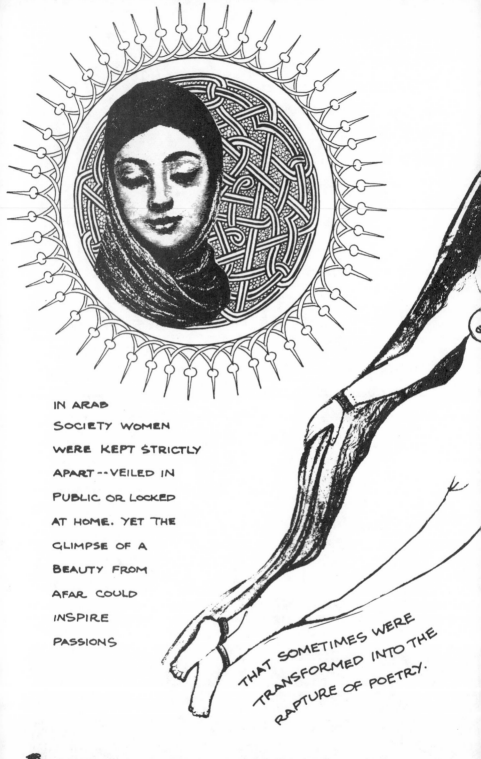

IN ARAB
SOCIETY WOMEN
WERE KEPT STRICTLY
APART -- VEILED IN
PUBLIC OR LOCKED
AT HOME. YET THE
GLIMPSE OF A
BEAUTY FROM
AFAR COULD
INSPIRE
PASSIONS

THAT SOMETIMES WERE
TRANSFORMED INTO THE
RAPTURE OF POETRY.

"WHEN I CONTEMPLATE THY CHEEK,
FORMED IN THE IMAGE OF THE MOON,
O' MY LOVE, IT IS IN TRUTH THE EFFECT
OF DIVINE GRACE
THAT I AM CONTEMPLATING."

FARTHER EAST IN INDIA, EROTIC ATTRACTION
WAS CONSIDERED THE DRIVING FORCE OF THE
UNIVERSE. AS THE HINDU SCRIPTURES SAY:
"IN THE BEGINNING WAS DESIRE."
EROTIC ENERGY WAS VENERATED AT INDIAN
TEMPLES IN THE FORM OF ICONS SHAPED
LIKE MALE AND FEMALE SEX ORGANS -- THE
LINGUM AND THE *YONI*. THE UNION OF
THESE OPPOSITES WAS EXPRESSED IN THE
HINDU CHANT **OM MANI PADME OM**:
THE JEWEL IS IN THE LOTUS, THE LINGUM
IN THE YONI.

EROTIC ART FLOURISHED IN THIS VOLUPTUOUS
CLIMATE. TEMPLE WALLS AT KHAJURAHO AND
KNONARAK ARE FILLED WITH AN UNDULATING
PROCESSION OF COSMIC LOVERS-- SENSUAL GODS
AND GODDESSES REPRESENTING THE INEXHAUSTIBLE
FERTILITY OF THE UNIVERSE.

"WHAT PLEASURES ARE YOU SEEKING FOR
YOURSELF?
ON WHOM IS THE SUN NOW RISING THAT WILL
ENJOY YOU?
WHO WILL DRINK HIS FILL OF THE LOTUS-PERFUMED
LIQUOR OF YOUR MOUTH?
...WHO WILL MOUNT SWIFTLY INTO YOUR BROAD
SECRET PARTS..."

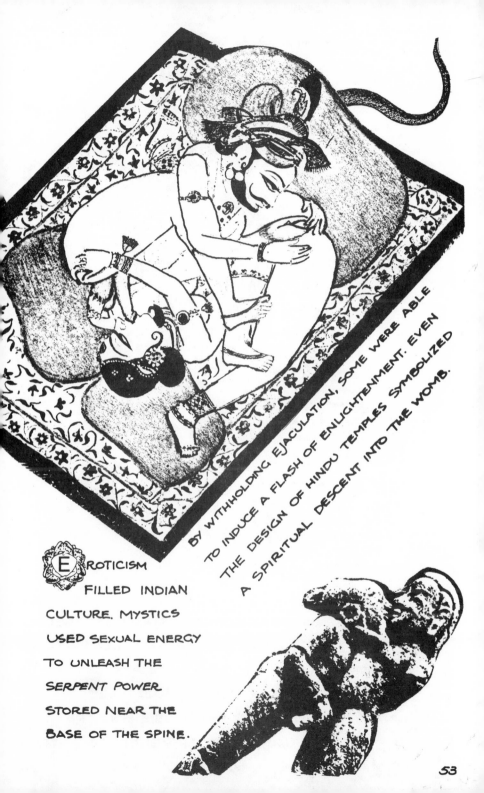

BY WITHHOLDING EJACULATION, SOME WERE ABLE TO INDUCE A FLASH OF ENLIGHTENMENT. EVEN THE DESIGN OF HINDU TEMPLES SYMBOLIZED A SPIRITUAL DESCENT INTO THE WOMB.

Eroticism FILLED INDIAN CULTURE. MYSTICS USED SEXUAL ENERGY TO UNLEASH THE SERPENT POWER STORED NEAR THE BASE OF THE SPINE.

IN CHINA, PHILOSOPHERS HAD LONG SEEN
LIFE AS A PROCESS OF CHANGE IN WHICH
OPPOSITES COME TOGETHER AND SEPARATE:
EARTH AND SKY, FEMALE AND MALE,
YIN AND *YANG*. EROTICISM FOR THE
CHINESE WAS A WAY OF REGULATING HEALTH,
AS WELL AS A SOURCE OF BEAUTY.

" THE BEAUTY OF WU OFFERS WINE
THE BEAUTY OF WU IS FIFTEEN YEARS
OLD, AND HER HAIR FLOATS IN
THE BREEZE;
HER CUP OF JADE INVITES THE GUEST
TO SAVOR THE WINE FROM THE
GRAPE. "

Europeans returning from the East brought with them a new taste for cleanliness, refinement, and pleasure. In France, troubador singers began to imitate the love poems they'd learned from the Arabs:

"FLORA FAULTLESS AS A BLOSSOM,

BARES HER SMOOTH LIMBS FOR MINE EYES;

SOFTLY SHINES HER VIRGIN BOSOM,

AND THE BREASTS THAT GENTLY RISE

LIKE THE HILLS OF PARADISE..

O, THE JOYS OF THIS POSSESSING

HOW UNSPEAKABLE THE BLESSING

SWEETEST SWEETS FROM FLORA FLOW."

"THE DEVIL IN THE FORM OF A GOAT, HAVING
   HIS MEMBER IN THE REAR,
   HAD INTERCOURSE WITH WOMEN
   BY JIGGLING   AND SHOVING
   THE THING
   AGAINST THEIR
   BELLY..."

THE GRADUAL REVIVAL OF
EUROPEAN CIVILIZATION WAS
ACCOMPANIED BY OUTBREAKS OF CRUELTY AND
MASS DELUSION: THE WITCH HUNTS. THE SUPPRESSED
EROTIC FEELINGS OF A CONTINENT NOW BURST
INTO A NIGHTMARE AS THE CHURCH TRANSFORMED
THE OLD NATURE GODS AND GODDESSES INTO
DEMONS.

OVER THE NEXT TWO CENTURIES HUNDREDS OF THOUSANDS OF WOMEN WERE ACCUSED OF HAVING SEX WITH DEMONS. THE USUAL PUNISHMENT INVOLVED TORTURE, FORCED CONFESSION, AND A PAINFUL DEATH BY BURNING AT THE STAKE.

YET NOTHING COULD STOP EUROPE'S REBIRTH OF TRADE AND CULTURE. FROM ITALY CAME A REDISCOVERY OF THE WONDERS OF PAST AGES. ROMAN LITERATURE, ARCHITECTURE, AND ART BECAME A MODEL FOR A REBIRTH, A *RENAISSANCE MAN,* NOT DIVINE SCRIPTURE, BECAME THE MEASURE OF ALL THINGS. AS THE ARTIST MICHAELANGELO DECLARED:

"NOR HATH GOD DEIGNED TO SHOW HIMSELF ELSEWHERE MORE CLEARLY THAN IN HUMAN

FORMS SUBLIME, WHICH, SINCE THEY IMAGE HIM, ALONE I LOVE."

THE HUMAN BODY WAS ONCE
AGAIN A FIT SUBJECT FOR ART.
TO AVOID ANGERING THE CHURCH,
RELIGIOUS THEMES WERE AT
FIRST CHOSEN AS TOPICS: SCENES
FROM THE OLD TESTAMENT,
AND THE NEW TESTAMENT...

59

AND FINALLY, THE
GODS, GODDESSES,
SATYRS, AND NYMPHS
OF PAGAN MYTHOLOGY.
THE SPIRIT OF
CHANGE
WAS IN THE AIR.

SHAKESPEARE FELT
BOLD ENOUGH TO WRITE LOVE SONNETS TO
SOMEONE CALLED THE DARK LADY, A
PERSON OF INDETERMINATE SEX:
"A WOMAN'S FACE, WITH NATURE'S OWN
 HAND PAINTED,
 HAST THOU, THE
 MASTER-MISTRESS
 OF MY PASSION."

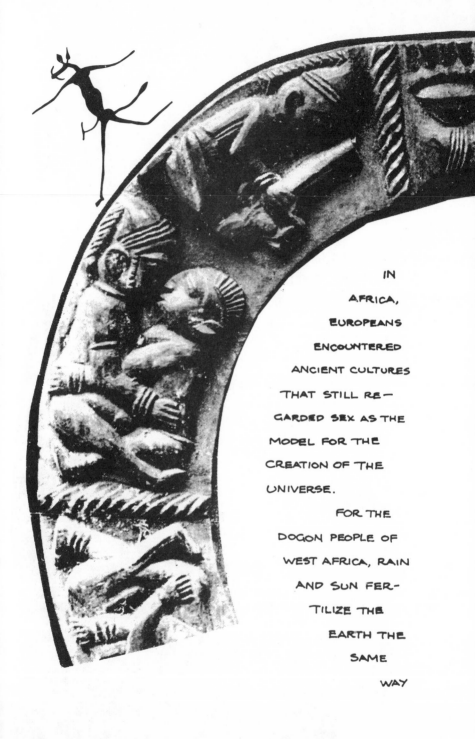

IN
AFRICA,
EUROPEANS
ENCOUNTERED
ANCIENT CULTURES
THAT STILL RE-
GARDED SEX AS THE
MODEL FOR THE
CREATION OF THE
UNIVERSE.

FOR THE
DOGON PEOPLE OF
WEST AFRICA, RAIN
AND SUN FER-
TILIZE THE
EARTH THE
SAME
WAY

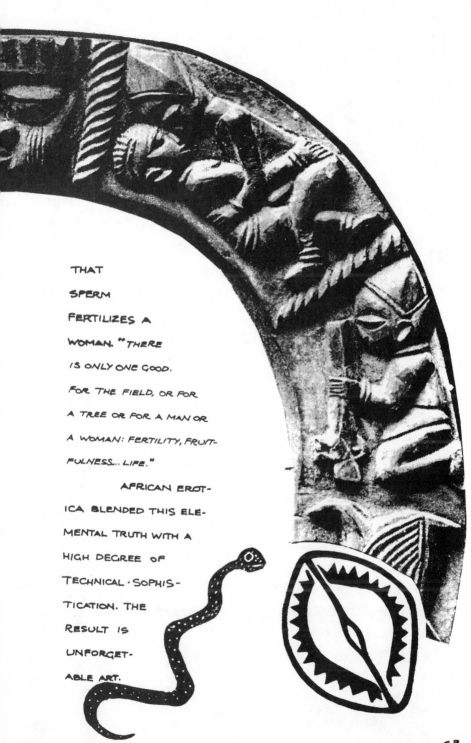

THAT
SPERM
FERTILIZES A
WOMAN. "THERE
IS ONLY ONE GOOD.
FOR THE FIELD, OR FOR
A TREE OR FOR A MAN OR
A WOMAN: FERTILITY, FRUIT-
FULNESS... LIFE."

AFRICAN EROT-
ICA BLENDED THIS ELE-
MENTAL TRUTH WITH A
HIGH DEGREE OF
TECHNICAL · SOPHIS-
TICATION. THE
RESULT IS
UNFORGET-
ABLE ART.

63

AFRICA'S ORAL TRADITION ALSO REFLECTS THE HEALTHY EROTICISM OF ITS PEOPLE.

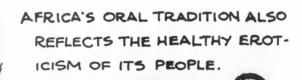

A CHARMING MANDE FOLK TALE TELLS OF A MAIDEN WHO REFUSED TO MARRY. A MAN WHO LOVED HER CHANGED HIMSELF INTO A FLUTE AND LAID HIMSELF BEFORE THE MAIDEN'S DOOR.

IT WAS THE LOVELIEST FLUTE SHE HAD EVER SEEN, AND THE MAIDEN HAPPILY TOOK IT INSIDE. THAT EVENING WHEN SHE LAY DOWN, THE FLUTE SPOKE: *"I WANT TO LIE DOWN ON THE BED, TOO."* THE MAIDEN TOLD HER MOTHER THAT THE FLUTE WAS A MAN.

"THERE'S NOTHING TO WORRY ABOUT," THE MOTHER REPLIED CALMLY.

WHEN THE MAIDEN UNDRESSED FOR SLEEP, THE FLUTE SAID, *"O, BUT I'D LIKE TO LAY BETWEEN YOUR BREASTS."* AGAIN THE GIRL RAN TO THE MOTHER AND TOLD HER THE FLUTE WAS A MAN. AND AGAIN THE MOTHER SAID, *"THERE'S NOTHING TO WORRY ABOUT."*

AS SOON AS THE MAIDEN PLACED THE
FLUTE BETWEEN HER BREASTS, IT TURNED
INTO A STRONG HANDSOME MAN WHO
MADE LOVE TO HER ALL NIGHT
LONG.

NEXT MORNING, THE MAIDEN TOLD HER MOTHER THAT
SHE WAS NOW MARRIED, SINCE THE FLUTE WAS A MAN.
"YOU SEE," THE MOTHER REPLIED COOLY, "THERE REALLY
WAS NOTHING TO WORRY ABOUT."

IN THE
AMERICAS,
EROTICA
WAS AS
VARIED AS
THE PEOPLE.
THE ANCIENT
OLMECS CARVED FER-
TILITY SYMBOLS SHOWING
SERPENTS, RAIN, SPROUT-
ING MAIZE, AND HUMAN
SEX ORGANS.

THE MAYA
SYMBOLIZED SEX WITH
FLOWERS AND ANIMALS
SUCH AS THE MONKEY,
WHICH ARE
OFTEN
SHOWN
FONDLING
WOMEN.

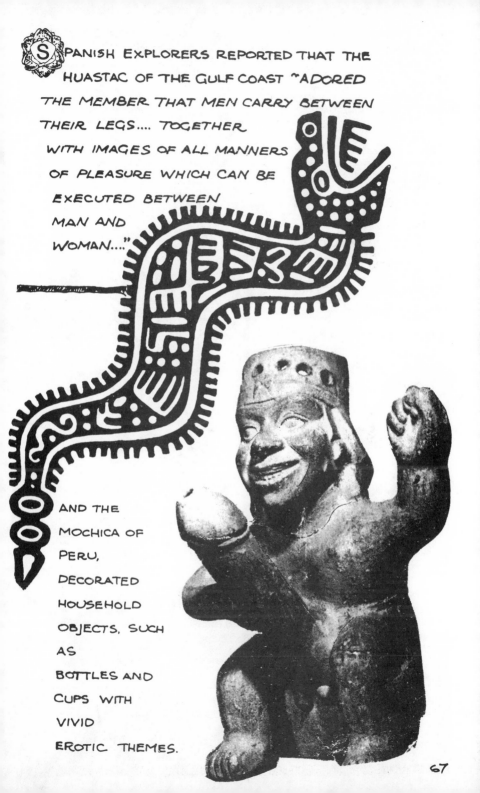

SPANISH EXPLORERS REPORTED THAT THE HUASTEC OF THE GULF COAST "ADORED THE MEMBER THAT MEN CARRY BETWEEN THEIR LEGS.... TOGETHER WITH IMAGES OF ALL MANNERS OF PLEASURE WHICH CAN BE EXECUTED BETWEEN MAN AND WOMAN...."

AND THE MOCHICA OF PERU, DECORATED HOUSEHOLD OBJECTS, SUCH AS BOTTLES AND CUPS WITH VIVID EROTIC THEMES.

67

IN THE 1700'S, EUROPEAN EROTICA WAS STILL A PRIVATE TASTE. KINGS HIRED COURT ARTISTS TO PAINT PORTRAITS OF THEIR LOVERS, WHICH WERE HUNG AS TROPHIES.

ENGRAVINGS SATIRIZING THE SEX LIVES OF THE RICH AND POWERFUL WERE ALSO SECRETLY DISTRIBUTED.

Count Donatien Alphonse de Sade (1740-1814), better known as the MARQUIS DE SADE, made it his life's work to explore the far boundaries of eroticism. In de Sade's writing, nothing is sacred except the truth that we are alone in this world and that our pleasure often depends on the pain of others. The only law is ABSOLUTE SELFISHNESS:

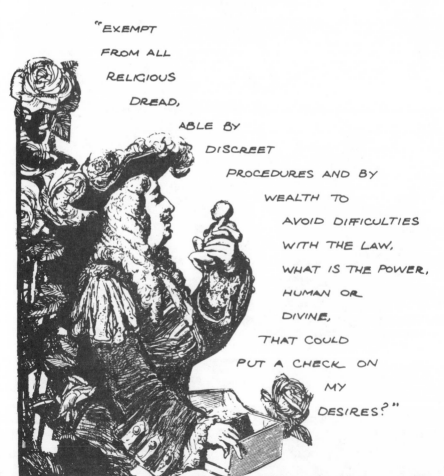

"Exempt from all religious dread, able by discreet procedures and by wealth to avoid difficulties with the law, what is the power, human or divine, that could put a check on my desires?"

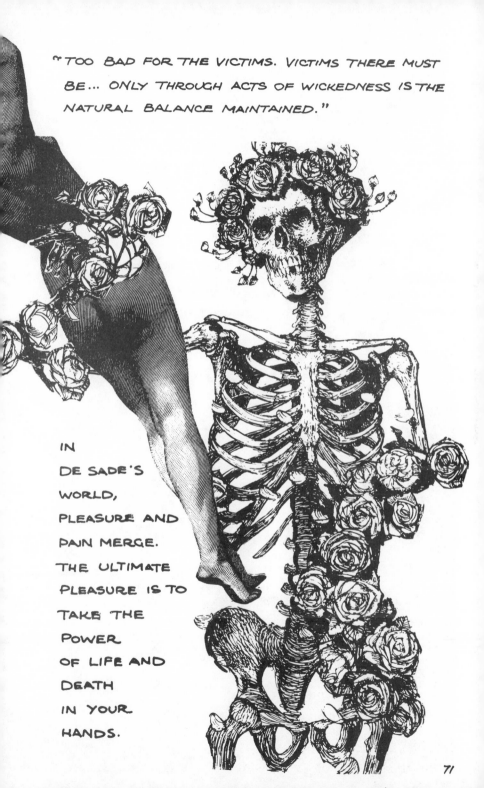

"TOO BAD FOR THE VICTIMS. VICTIMS THERE MUST BE... ONLY THROUGH ACTS OF WICKEDNESS IS THE NATURAL BALANCE MAINTAINED."

IN DE SADE'S WORLD, PLEASURE AND PAIN MERGE. THE ULTIMATE PLEASURE IS TO TAKE THE POWER OF LIFE AND DEATH IN YOUR HANDS.

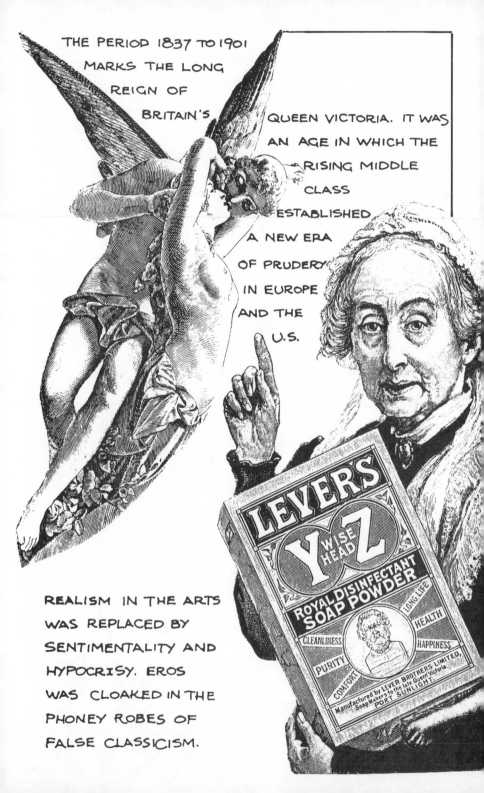

THE PERIOD 1837 TO 1901 MARKS THE LONG REIGN OF BRITAIN'S QUEEN VICTORIA. IT WAS AN AGE IN WHICH THE RISING MIDDLE CLASS ESTABLISHED A NEW ERA OF PRUDERY IN EUROPE AND THE U.S.

REALISM IN THE ARTS WAS REPLACED BY SENTIMENTALITY AND HYPOCRISY. EROS WAS CLOAKED IN THE PHONEY ROBES OF FALSE CLASSICISM.

LEVERS Y WISE HEAD Z
ROYAL DISINFECTANT SOAP POWDER
CLEANLINESS · PURITY · COMFORT · LONG LIFE · HEALTH · HAPPINESS
Manufactured by LEVER BROTHERS LIMITED, Soap Makers to the late Queen Victoria PORT SUNLIGHT.

THE UPLIFTING OF PUBLIC MORALS BECAME THE OFFICIAL FUNCTION OF ART. IN THIS PERIOD, THERE WAS EVEN A TABOO AGAINST SHOWING PUBIC HAIR, WHICH WOULD ONLY REMIND PEOPLE OF THEIR BESTIAL ORIGINS.

YET, UNOFFICIALLY, PROSTITUTION FLOURISHED. AND SECRETLY, ARTISTS CIRCULATED EROTIC NOVELS AND ENGRAVINGS IN EVER GREATER NUMBERS.

THE EROTIC IMAGINATION BECAME INFUSED WITH SELF-LOATHING AND SADISM. WOMEN WERE SEEN AS AVENGING ANGELS, WHIP IN HAND, OR AS HEARTLESS DEMONS LEADING MEN TO DESTRUCTION. HERE IS HOW THE VICTORIAN POET SWINBURNE DESCRIBED HIS OWN *FEMME FATALE,* DOLORES, LADY OF SENSUAL PAIN:

"COLD EYELIDS THAT HID LIKE A JEWEL HARD EYES THAT GROW SOFT FOR AN HOUR, THE HEAVY WHITE LIMBS AND THE CRUEL RED MOUTH LIKE A VENOMOUS FLOWER."

"HE HUGS ME TIGHT, OUR NOSES TOUCH. I AM AS HAPPY AS HE IS. WE PUT OUR TONGUES IN EACH OTHER'S MOUTHS. HE LIES ON MY BREAST; HE TELLS ME HOW HAPPY HE IS."

IN THE LATE 1890'S, PAINTER PAUL GAUGUIN DISCOVERED THAT A HEALTHY EROTICISM STILL SURVIVED IN THE ISLANDS OF POLYNESIA -- DESPITE A CENTURY OF COLONIZERS AND MISSIONARIES. THE OLD WAYS WERE PRE- SERVED IN MYTHS AND POPULAR CUSTOMS, AS WELL AS BY THE ARTS OF TATTOOING, SCULPTURE AND THE SEDUCTIVE DANCES, LIKE THE HULA.

"GIVE ME YOUR BODY... YOU ARE AS FAIR AS THE SANDS ON THE BEACH."

ON THE ISLANDS OF JAPAN, EROTICA HAD LONG BEEN VALUED BOTH FOR ITS OWN SAKE AND AS A SEXUAL GUIDE. PILLOW-BOOKS, SCROLLS OF EROTIC PRINTS USED IN THE BEDROOM, DATE BACK TO THE 13TH CENTURY.

SHUNGA IS THE NAME FOR THESE EROTIC PRINTS. THEY ARE BOLD GRAPHIC STATEMENTS WHICH DO NOT SHOW SEX AS A ROMANTIC IDEAL OR RELIGIOUS ACT. INSTEAD, THEY FOCUS ON THE THE PLEASURES OF THE SEX ACT.

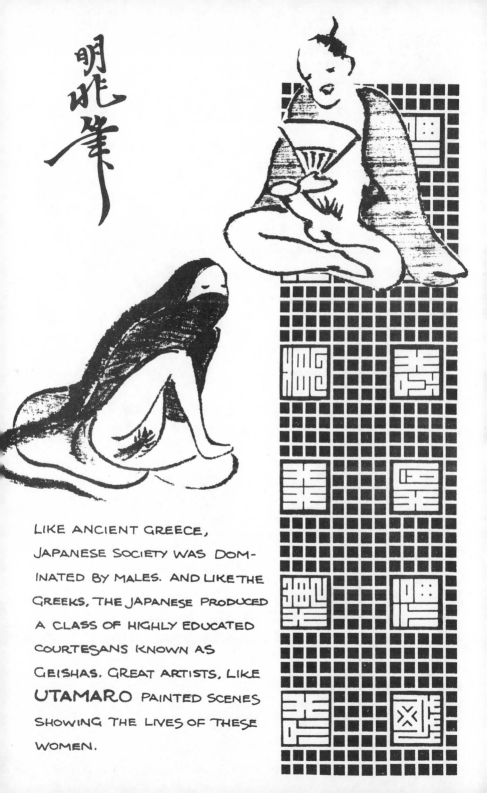

LIKE ANCIENT GREECE,
JAPANESE SOCIETY WAS DOM-
INATED BY MALES. AND LIKE THE
GREEKS, THE JAPANESE PRODUCED
A CLASS OF HIGHLY EDUCATED
COURTESANS KNOWN AS
GEISHAS. GREAT ARTISTS, LIKE
UTAMARO PAINTED SCENES
SHOWING THE LIVES OF THESE
WOMEN.

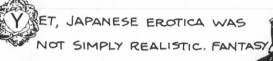

Y ET, JAPANESE EROTICA WAS
NOT SIMPLY REALISTIC. FANTASY
WAS ALSO AN IMPORTANT
FEATURE. THE SIZE OF
MALE AND FEMALE
SEX ORGANS, FOR
EXAMPLE, WERE
OFTEN
EXAGGERATED.

A TASTE
FOR SADISM
IS SOMETIMES
REVEALED IN THE
SCENES OF RAPE --
USUALLY BY BANDITS OR
UNCOUTH FOREIGNERS.

JAPANESE ARTISTS ALSO PROBED THE COMIC SIDE OF SEXUALITY, WHILE MASTERS SUCH AS **HOKUSAI** DELVED INTO THE EROTIC MYSTERIES OF DREAMS.

I N THE WEST, THE
TWENTIETH CENTURY
BROUGHT A NEW EROTIC FRANK-
NESS. GERMAN PAINTERS WERE
AMONG THE FIRST TO EXPLORE
THE WILD, ELEMENTAL POWER OF
SEXUALITY. IN THE WORK OF
EGON SCHIELE, THE HUMAN
FORM WAS AT LAST STRIPPED
OF ALL FALSE
SENTIMENTALITY.

AFTER THE SAVAGERY OF WORLD WAR I, GERMAN ARTISTS SUCH AS **GEORG GROSZ** USED SCENES OF SEXUAL DOMINATION TO ATTACK OTHER FORMS OF INHUMANITY AND OPPRESSION -- SOCIAL AND POLITICAL.

PABLO PICASSO RETURNED TO THE MYTHIC WORLD OF THE PAST IN ORDER TO EXPLORE HUMANITY'S EROTIC FUTURE...

"ART IS NOT CHASTE."

SURREALIST PAINTERS USED COMPLEX EROTIC
IMAGES TO PROBE THE SYMBOLIC DREAM WORLD
OF THE UNCONSCIOUS.

ÉALISTE

SUR

IN MODERN TIMES, MORE PEOPLE THAN EVER EXPERIENCE EROTICA IN THE FORM OF MASS-PRODUCED PHOTOS, PRINTS, MUSIC, AND MOVIES. THE QUALITY--AS IN ANY POPULAR ART-- RANGES FROM CRUDE TO DELIGHTFULLY SOPHISTICATED.

YET FAR MORE PEOPLE ARE EXPOSED TO THE SEXUAL IMAGERY FOUND IN ADVERTISING AND MODERN PRODUCT DESIGN. EROTICISM IS USED AND EXCITEMENT TO

IN TODAY'S WORLD, TO IMPART GLAMOUR EVERYTHING FROM LITE BEER TO HEAVY MACHINERY.

(Y)ET, FOR THE ARTIST, THE EROTIC IMAGINATION CONTINUES AS A RICH, ENDURING SOURCE OF INSPIRATION. LET POET **ALLEN GINSBERG** HAVE THE FINAL WORD:

"THE WARM BODIES
   SHINE TOGETHER
IN THE DARKNESS,
   THE HAND MOVES
TO THE CENTER
   OF THE FLESH,
THE SKIN TREMBLES
   IN HAPPINESS
AND THE SOUL COMES
   JOYFUL TO THE EYE -
YES, YES
   THAT'S WHAT
I WANTED,
   I ALWAYS WANTED.
I ALWAYS WANTED,
   TO RETURN
TO THE BODY
   WHERE I WAS BORN."

THE EROTIC IMPULSE CANNOT BE LEGISLATED AWAY. IT IS OUR BIRTHRIGHT.

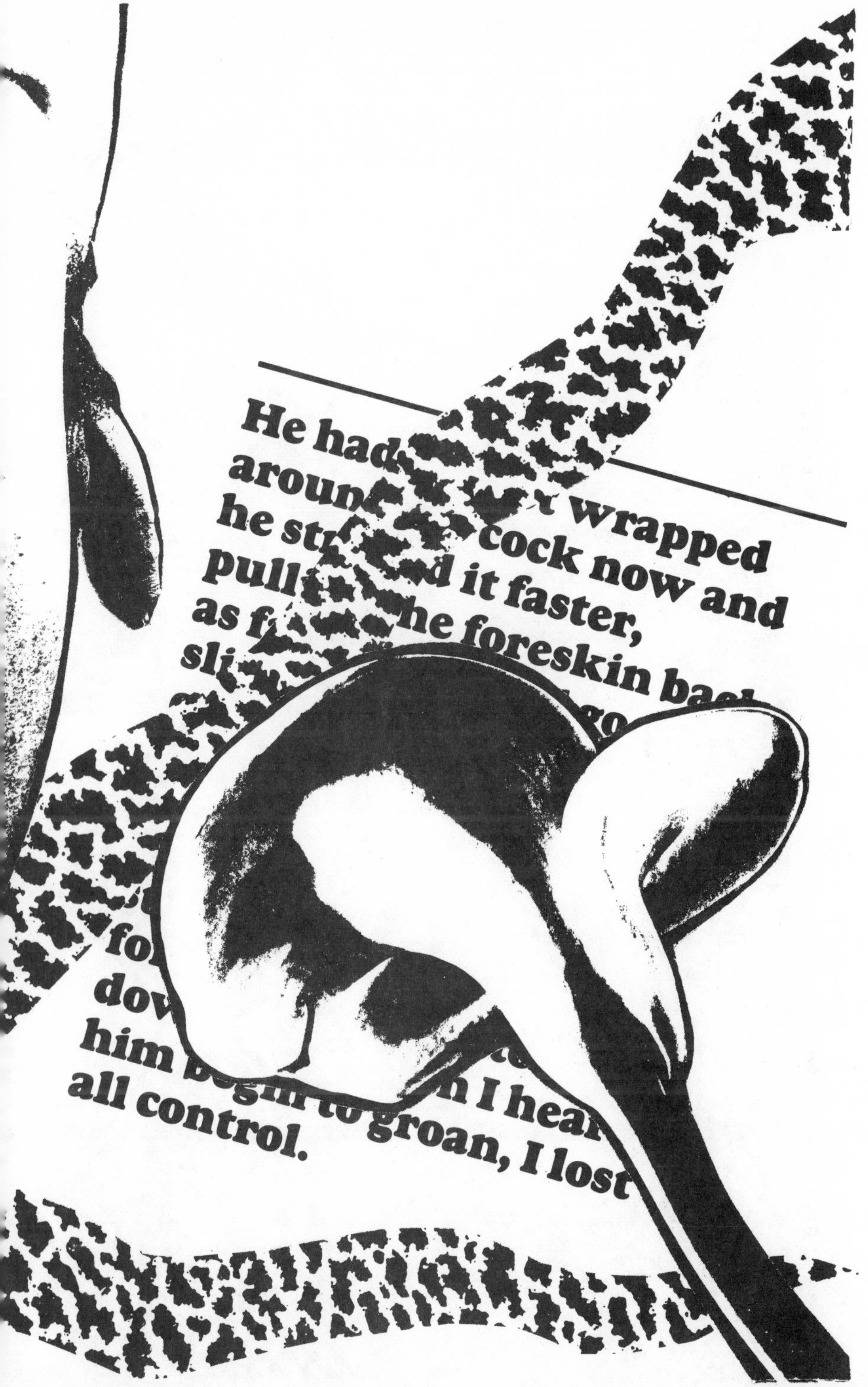

He had ... wrapped
aroun... ...cock now and
he str... ...d it faster,
pull... ...e foreskin bac...
as f... ...
sli...

fo...
dov...
him b...g... to groan, I hea...
all control.

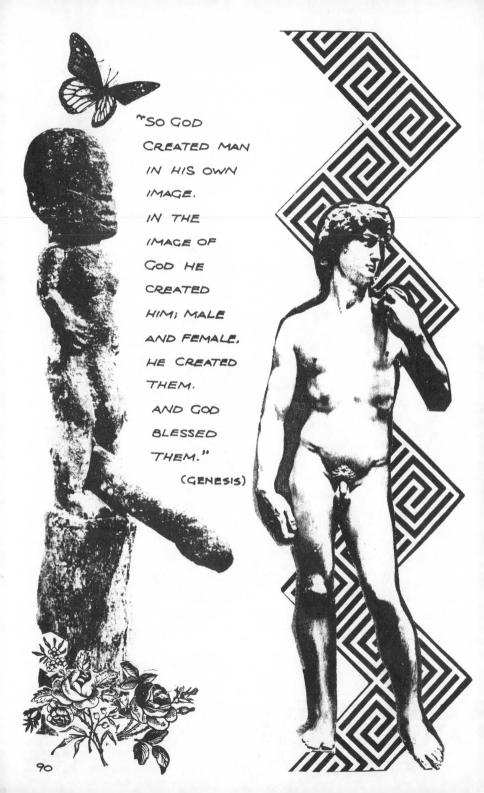

"SO GOD
CREATED MAN
IN HIS OWN
IMAGE.
IN THE
IMAGE OF
GOD HE
CREATED
HIM; MALE
AND FEMALE,
HE CREATED
THEM.
AND GOD
BLESSED
THEM."

(GENESIS)

REFERENCES

Page 4,5/Bookplate: Mark Severin; illustration Gustave Klimt; Bkplate: A. Baldinelli

Page 6,7/Penthouse Pet collage; painting: Prud'hon; illust: Tom of Finland

Page 8, 9/Painting collage: Robert Shelley; Photo: Robert Maplethorpe

Page ll/Bookplate: Giorgio Balbi

Page 12, 13/Venus of Willendorf (30,000 B.C); Venus of Lascaux (17,000B.C); prehistoric wall painting of ritual sex act

Page 14, 15/Mediterranean Goddess figurines (7-2,000B.C); Rock engraving, Fezzan, Libya (5,000 B.C.)

Page 17/Payrus of Tameniu, Egypt (1100 - 950B.C.)

Page 18, 19/Turin erotic papyrus; Tomb painting, Thebes, Egypt

Page 21/Statue of Ishtar (1500 - 1000 B.C.)

Page 22, 23/Statue of Cathaginian Astarte, collage with mural of tree of life; statue of Ishtar

Page 27/Minoan wall paintings, Knosos (1,700 - 1,400 B.C.)

Page 28, 29/Marble pillar herme, Siphnos, Greece (520 B.C.) Aphrodite and Eros detail from engraved metal plate

Page 30, 31/Athenian and Attic cup and pot designs, Fifth Century B.C

Page 32, 33/Illust of Lysistrata: Ivan Grazni

Page 34, 35/Athenian pottery details; illustration:Aristide Maillol

Page 36,37/Statue, House of Vetii, Pompei; Arretine Bowl Stamp.

Page38,39/Details from tile work, Pompei, 1st Century, A.D.

Page 41 / Illustrations:Titian

Page 42/ St. Jerome: Titian

Pages 44, 45/ Martyrs : Titian; demon engravings: Nicolas de Rouges, 1496

Page 48,49/Two lovers: Muhammad Quasin

Page 50, 51/Indian print of lovers, 1840; wall statuary, Khajurho, 1000 A.d.

Page 52, 53/Temple goddess stautue, Tiruranamalai; Bundi miniature painting of lovers.

Page 54, 55/Silk paintings, late 17th Century, China

FOR FURTHER READING

CAUGHT LOOKING: Feminism, Pornography, and Censorship
Eitors Kate Ellis, Nan Hunter, Caught Looking, Inc., NY
1986

THE COMPLETE BOOK OF EROTIC ART
Compiled by Drs. Phyllis and Eberhard Kronhausen (Vol 1 & 2), Bell Publishing, NY 1970.

EROTIC ART
Richard Bentley
Gallery Books, New York, 1984

EROTIC ARTS
Peter Webb, New York Graphic Society Books, 1975

EROS IN ANTIQUITY
Photos Antonia Mulas, The Erotic Book Society, New York, 1978

THE GOLDEN ASS
Apuleius, trans Jack Lindsay, Indiana University Press, Bloomington, Il. 1960

ROBERT MAPLETHORPE
Photos by Robert Maplethorpe Whitney Museum of American Art, 1988

ORIENTAL EROTIC ART
Philip Rawson, Gallery Book, New York, 1981

WOMEN'S IMAGES OF MEN
Ed. S. Kent & J. Morreau
Writers & Readers Publishing
New York, London, 1985

SEX
FOR BEGINNERS

ERROL SELKIRK

This is a beautifully illustrated, often humorous "documentary comic book" that explores human sexuality from the viewpoints of history, social relations, and sexual politics.

What is the link between sex and power? Do men and women have different attitudes toward pleasure? Why is sex used so often in advertising?

Readers will delight as diverse authorities such as Sade, Freud, and Reich trade provocative views on love and Eros.

Writers and Readers Beginners Books

African History for Beginners ....8.95 _____
Architecture for Beginners...7.95 _____
Black History for Beginners...7.95 _____
Black Women for Beginners...8.95 _____
The Brain for Beginners ....8.95 _____
Brecht for Beginners ....7.95 _____
Capitalism for Beginners ....6.95 _____
Computers for Beginners ....7.95 _____
Cuba for Beginners ....6.95 _____
Darwin for Beginners...6.95 _____
DNA for Beginners ....6.95 _____
Ecology for Beginners ....6.95 _____
Economists for Beginners ....4.95 _____
Einstein for Beginners...6.95 _____
Elvis for Beginners ....6.95 _____
Erotica for Beginners...8.95 _____
Food for Beginners..7.95 _____
French Revolution for Beginners..7.95 _____
Freud for Beginners ....6.95 _____
Hemingway for Beginners ....8.95 _____
Ireland for Beginners...6.95 _____
Judaism for Beginners ....7.95 _____
Lenin for Beginners ....6.95 _____
London for Beginners...6.95 _____
Malcolm X for Beginners ....8.95 _____
Mao for Beginners...6.95 _____
Marx for Beginners..6.95 _____
Marx for Beginners (Second Edition) ....8.95 _____
Marx's *Kapital* for Beginners ....6.95 _____
Media and Communications for Beginners ....8.95 _____
Medicine for Beginners ....4.95 _____
Nicaragua for Beginners ....7.95 _____
Nietzsche for Beginners ....7.95 _____
Nuclear Power for Beginners ....6.95 _____
Orwell for Beginners..4.95 _____
Pan-Africanism for Beginners ....8.95 _____
Peace for Beginners..6.95 _____
Philosophy for Beginners ....8.95 _____
Plato for Beginners..7.95 _____
Psychiatry for Beginners ....6.95 _____
Rainforests for Beginners..8.95 _____
Reagan for Beginners ....4.95 _____
Reich for Beginners...6.95 _____
Sex for Beginners..7.95 _____
Socialism for Beginners ....6.95 _____
Trotsky for Beginners ....6.95 _____
U.S. Constitution for Beginners..7.95 _____
Virginia Woolf for Beginners..7.95 _____
World War II for Beginners ....8.95 _____
Zen for Beginners..6.95 _____